paul weller heavy soul

  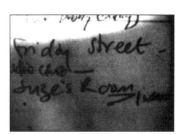

Wise Publications
London/New York/Sydney/Paris/Copenhagen/Madrid

Exclusive Distributors:
Music Sales Limited
8-9 Frith Street, London W1V 5TZ, England.
Music Sales Pty Limited
120 Rothschild Avenue, Rosebery, NSW 2018,
Australia.

Order No. AM950158
ISBN 0-7119-7005-X

Visit the Internet Music Shop at
http:. www.musicsales.co.uk

Music arranged by Roger Day.
Music processed by Paul Ewers Music Design.

Printed in the United Kingdom by
Halstan & Co. Limited, Amersham, Buckinghamshire.

Heavy Soul (PT 1)

Words & Music by Paul Weller

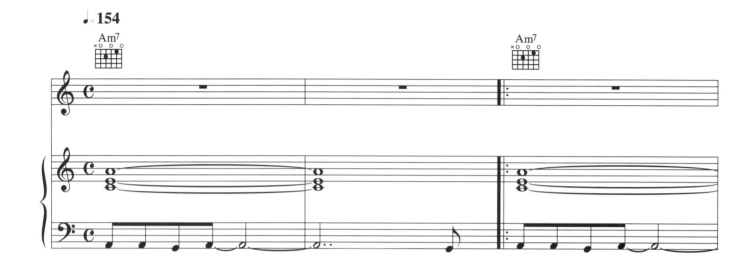

1. We're
(Verses 2 & 3 see block lyric)

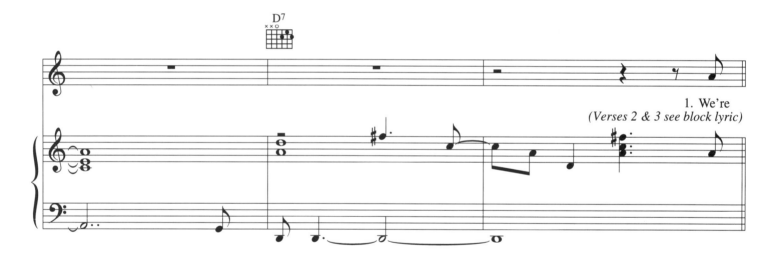

words up-on a win-dow,   writ-ten there___ in steam,

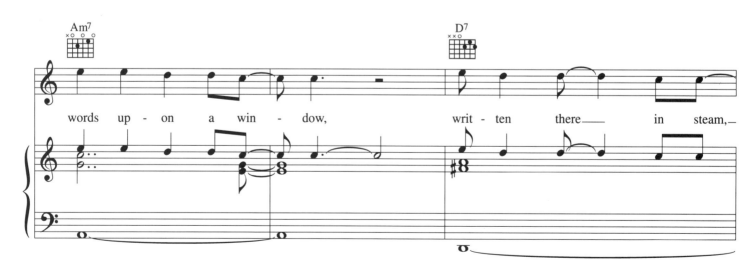

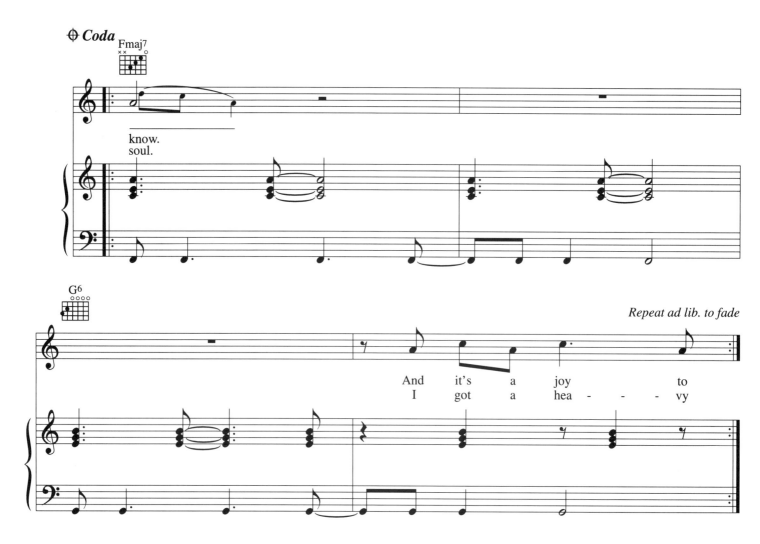

Verse 2:
Tuesday's dressed in shearling
Anchored on belief
In the sunlight on the water
Or rain upon a leaf
And I'm touched by its beauty
And I hope to touch you too
'Cause I still seek the same things
That I once sought to be true.

And you know
That's where the wind blows
Though I wouldn't be lying
When I tell you that I
Got a heavy soul.

Verse 3:
We're words upon a window
Written there in steam
In the heat of a moment
Everything is what it seems
Vapours passing nearly
So I'm touched by the thought
That I can't be beaten
And I can't be bought.

And you'll know
It's a joy to know
I don't think I'd be lying
When I tell you that I
Got a heavy soul.

8

Peacock Suit

Words & Music by Paul Weller

1. I've got a grape - fruit mat - ter,_____
(Verses 2 & 3 see block lyric)

____ it's as sour__ as shit.____ I have no____

In my pea-cock suit_____ I look real cute.—

(Ad lib. vocal)

Fade

Verse 2:
I'm Narcissus in a puddle,
In shop windows I gloat.
Like a ball of fleece lining
In my camel skin coat.
I don't need a ship
To sail in stormy weather;
Don't need you to ruffle the feathers
Of my peacock suit.
Did you think I should?

Verse 3:
Nemesis in a muddle,
In a mirror I look.
Lke a streak of sheet light'nin'
In my rattlesnake shoes.
I don't need a ship
To sail in stormy weather;
Don't need you to ruffle the feathers
Of my peacock suit.
Did you think I should?

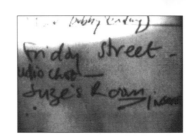

Up In Suzes' Room

Words & Music by Paul Weller

bloom-ing - ful,_____ I'm up in Su-zes'— room_____

where life goes so soon.

(2.) She's

Soon a - gainst the moon a big sky paints, but she calls— the tunes,—

she's cool that way,_____ how I wish__ it could

stay_____

for - ev - er that way.

F#m9

B9

D.𝄋. al Coda

Verse 2:
She's anything that you can call free
She's everything that she wants to be
She has everything that you could want to see.

I'm up in Suzes' room, flowers bloomingful
I'm up in Suzes' room where life goes so soon.

Verse 3:
No one moves, no one can
Luck rolls its coins, they land where they stand
To make us everything that you never planned.

I'm up in Suzes' room, people bloomingful
Yes, yes in Suzes' room where life goes so soon.

Brushed

Words & Music by Paul Weller, Steve White & Mark Nelson

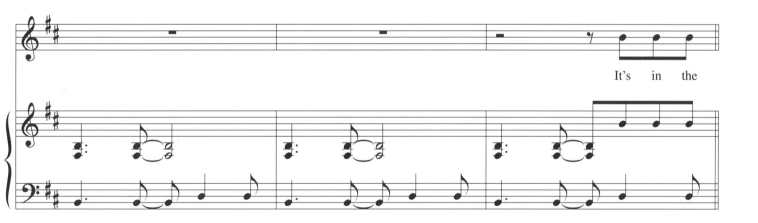

It's in the

stroke of a brush, ___ it's in the wave of a hand, ___
verse that you read, ___ it's in the tune in your head,

Luck-y to be

Driving Nowhere

Words & Music by Paul Weller

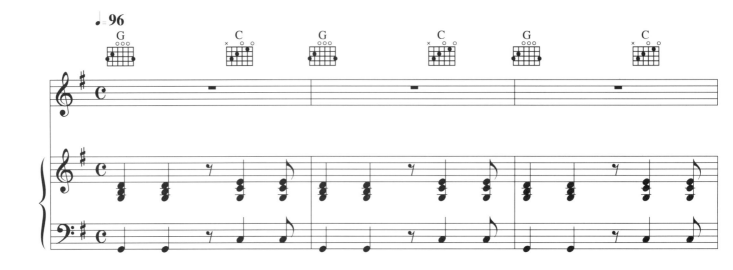

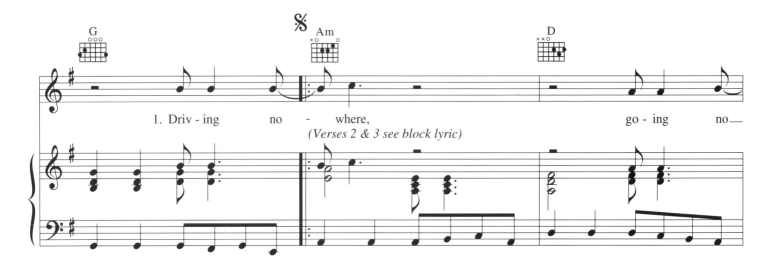

Verse 2:
Pleasure sifting – can you keep it
And as I'm drifting – it's hard to feel it
I feel I'm floating in a time
Driving nowhere – along for a ride

Verse 3:
Driving nowhere – gettin' someplace
I get restless – I'm still curious
And I'm waiting for a tide
To take me nowhere – along for a ride

I Should Have Been There To Inspire You

Words & Music by Paul Weller

Nothing I'd say or I____ could do____ could move the
I nev-er took the time to see____ how you'd grown,____ I nev-er took the

moun-tains from your view,____ noth-ing I see or I____ could show,____ there's on-ly
care it takes to know,____ nev-er took the time to see____ what you found, but al-ways had the

Oh— I be-lieved in you— girl,_____ girl, I be-lieved in you.—

Repeat ad lib. to fade

Heavy Soul (PT 2)

Words & Music by Paul Weller

Friday Street

Words & Music by Paul Weller

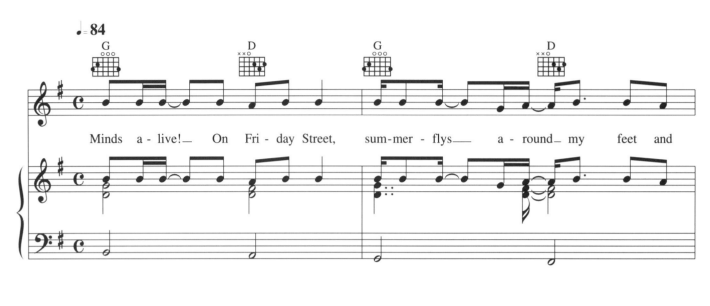

Minds a - live!__ On Fri - day Street, sum - mer - flys__ a - round__ my feet and

wee still stars are in__ my eyes,__ and mine's a - live__ on Fri - day Street.

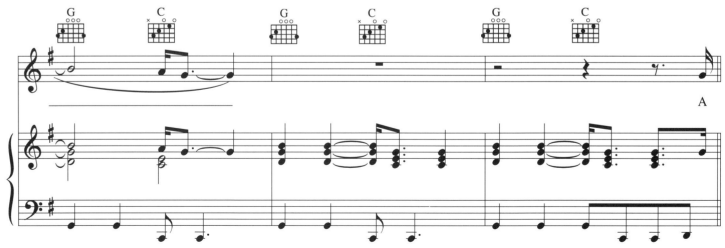

Lives a-live on Friday Street, you start to shine in a brand new heat, and the world

is clear, like you're not real-ly here, and I see

my-self and I'm real-ly not scared.

Mine's still a-live on Fri-day Street.

Mine's a-live on Friday Street. It's like

plug-ging back in on Fri-day Street.

May it

al-ways come a-live on Fri-day Street.

Science

Words & Music by Paul Weller

1. I have my thoughts to po - si - tion,
(Verses 2 & 3 see block lyrics)

but do I know how to act? I have no

Verse 2:
I'm a piece of the earth
I take no offence
I can be who I am
I have no pretence.
Only to what you can be
If you want to be
It's a way of living

Verse 3:
So grab a piece in the air
Try and make it sing
Try and be who you can
It's the real, real thing
I'm into what you can be
If you want to be
As a way of living.

Chorus 2:
I've got a pick in my pocket, does that make me a player?
Words can't do what action does louder.
Putting on gloves doesn't make me a fighter
And all the study in the world doesn't make it science.

Golden Sands

Words & Music by Paul Weller

1. Try, try if you can
2. ____ (Verses 2 & 3 see block lyric)

try and get your back up and off the gold - en sands.

Try to get some - where

that you've nev - er   been____   as you sit up - on the

F   Fm   A♭
fr4

green__ grass,   there's still so much to   see____   and find__

Am   B♭   C

____ your - self   wait - ing just to try, try,   try.____

1.   2, 3.   A♭
fr4

(2.) Just what you want____   To find__ my - self   wait -

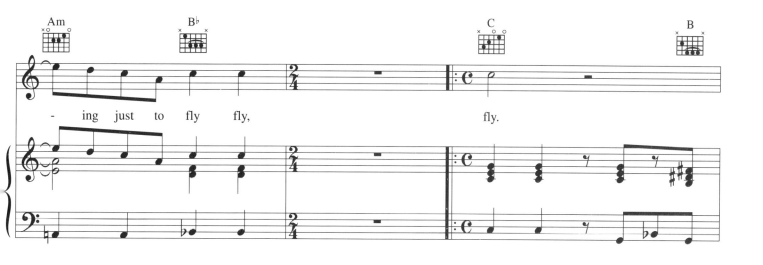

- ing just to fly fly, fly.

Repeat to fade

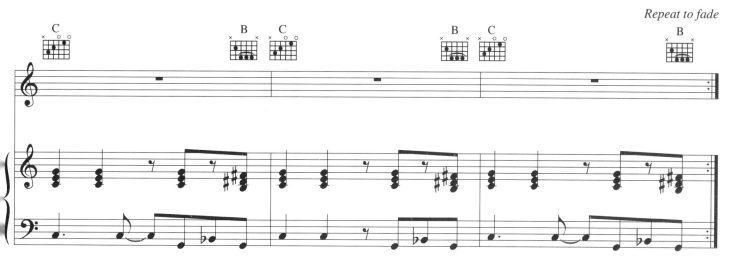

Verse 2:
Just what you want
Is just what you'll get
As you fall upon the real path
Or take a safer bet.

And you can give everything
Still none comes to you
You can hang life round your neck, y'all
I may hang there too
And find myself
Waiting just to try, try, try.

Verse 3:
Try, try if you can
Got to get your back up
And off the golden sands.

Just don't remember
If only for you
You can hang life round your neck, y'all
Or you can be there too
And find yourself
Waiting just to fly, fly, fly.
To find yourself
Waiting just to fly, fly… fly.

As You Lean Into The Light

Words & Music by Paul Weller

1. Gen - tle rain,—
(Verses 2 & 3 see block lyric)

here it comes a - gain,—

from your eyes _____ and I'd wash a - way ___ the emp-

Verse 2:
Hail and stone
And all that's gone
When everything that passes cuts to the bone.
Turning like a wheel dragging a heavy stone
A weight that ties you down that you will never own.

Verse 3:
Strange to see
A paper smile on thee
When once you moved and lit the room for us all to be
Now if I could be the sun I'd shine in your life
If I could be the rain I'd rain from your eyes.

And I'd wash away the emptiness you feel inside.

Mermaids

Words & Music by Paul Weller

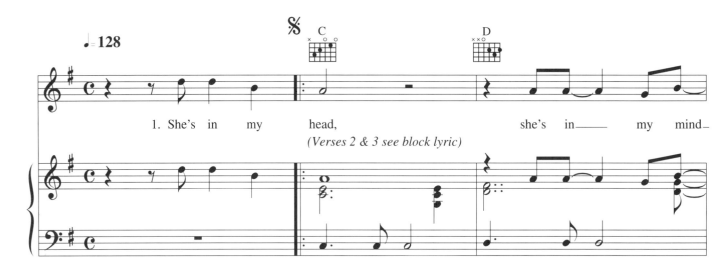

1. She's in my head, she's in — my mind —

(Verses 2 & 3 see block lyric)

and I'm all she says, —

yes she knows — me well, — as well — as you can

take it all,_____ I

want to know_____ what lies be-hind_____

your___ smiles___ and shells, wish I knew___ you well._

D.%. al Coda

Come in___ my head___

Sha la la la la.

Verse 2:
She's on my side
I often hide
In her magic hair
And there I learn again
The joy of life.

Verse 3:
Come in my head
Come in my mind
You can only love
When you open up
To be yourself.